EPHESOS

The Mystery of the Bee

SARA PARDO

Illustrations: Zeynep Gargi

ARKEOLOJİ
VE SANAT
ÇOCUK
YAYINLARI

ARCHAEOLOGY & ART CHILDREN'S PUBLICATIONS

E P H E S O S
The Mystery of the Bee

Sara PARDO

Editor
Nezih BAŞGELEN

Translation
Bilgi ALTINOK

Illustrations
Zeynep GARGİ

Printing: Özgün Ofset
Yeşilce Mah. Aytekin Sok. No: 21, 4. Levent-İstanbul
Phone: (0212) 280 00 09

ISBN: 978-605-396-112-3

Bookstore:

arkeopera www.arkeopera.com
Yeniçarşı Cad. No: 16/A, 34433 Galatasaray, İstanbul
Phone: 0 212 249 92 26   Fax: 0 212 244 31 64
www.arkeolojisanat.com / info@arkeolojisanat.com

Not obliged to bear a label within the framework of the second paragraph of the 5th article of the
Regulations about the Procedures and Basis related with the Application of Label.

Foreword

Dear Kids,

We prepared this book with care and had great fun writing and illustrating it. We hope that you too will share our feelings while reading it.

The "bee" was the symbol of the city of Ephesos. However **The Mystery of the Bee** is just an imaginary detective story. Nevertheless, all the historical, geographical, archaeological, artistic, cultural and mythological information given in this book, is correct. Let us express it this way: kids, you all can be tour guides after reading and clearly understanding this book. But, hold on a moment! There are a lot more things for you to see and learn. Let this book be a beginning and a source of inspiration for your love of history and archaeology. First of all there will be words and names you would not know or understand while reading the story. To truly enjoy what you ar reading, refer to the **Dictionary of Mythology**, **Dictionary of Archaeology**, and **Basic Information** pages at the end of the book.

Dear children, our country is full of historical sites of pirceless beauty and unmatched values. Learn about this heritage; love and protect it with the respect it deserves.

Let **The Mystery of the Bee** be my gift to all the children of the world.

Acknowledgement

I thank my dear friend Nilgün Şirin who gave me this mission years ago by putting a comic book in front of me and saying, "Sara, you have been a tour guide in Ephesos for forty years. You have a mission now, to write and prepare a comic book about Ephesos for youngsters". Now I am happy to have accomplished this mission. I extend my love and thanks to my husband Jaki; my daughter Sonia Amado who always guided me; to my grandchildren, Can, Deniz, and Selen who assisted me with their fresh ideas; my whole family and friends; Tülin and Steven Levitas and Eti Tuvi for re-editing; besides my special thanks to Sema and Nezih Başgelen with their family of "Archaeology and Art Children's Publications" for their enthusiasm, support, and meticulous work in preparing and publishing this book.

Our adventure takes place in the town of Selçuk, situated on the coast of the Aegean Sea, in west Anatolia (Turkey). The coastal region of Anatolia is so beautiful and so fertile that for thousands of years, hundreds of tribes migrated from all directions and founded many civilizations in this land. İzmir, the most prominant city of this region, and its vicinity have a history of at least 8500 years. The first local tribes were the Leleges and the Carians. Thousands of years later, begining from 1200 B.C., the Aeolians, Ionians, and Dorians came from Greece and established many small city states. Eventually, those cities were abandoned for reasons such as earthquakes and epidemics, and only their ruins remained. While most cities remain lost under the ground, some have been partly unearthed by the archeologists. Our story begins, in one of these cities: the magnificent city of Ephesos. Today it is visited and admired by people from all around the world. Founded in the valley between Mt. Pion and Mt. Koressos, Ephesos had two harbors. The Kaistros River flowing nearby, filled the gulf constantly with silt. The city was abandoned by the 8. century. Most of the inhabitants moved to Ayasuluk. In 1869, a British Engineer, James Turtle Wood who was building a railroad discovered the site of the Temple of Artemis situated outside the city. The temple is considered as one of the Seven Wonders of the Ancient World. The Austrian archaeologists started the excavations in ancient Ephesos in 1895 and found the remains of the city. Today only one third of Ephesos is brought to light. Come on Youngsters! Let's start reading our story and visiting famous Ephesos.

ONE DAY WHILE ALI EFFENDI WAS WORKING IN HIS FIELD IN SELÇUK, THE TIP OF HIS PICK STUCK TO SOMETHING. WHEN HE CONTINUED TO DIG...

HE SAW, GUESS WHAT? A RUSTED AND ROTTEN CHEST WAS LYING IN THE PIT

AFTER STRIVING A LITTLE, ALI EFFENDI OPENED THE LID OF THE CHEST. THERE WAS A SCROLL OF THICK PAPER FALLING TO PIECES IN IT.

ALI EFFENDI COULD NOT READ THE SCRIPT AND HE SHOWED THE SCROLL TO HIS SONS. WHEN THEY ALSO COULD NOT UNDERSTAND ANYTHING...

HE WENT TO THE GOVERNOR TO ASK FOR ADVICE. HE, TOO, WAS VERY SURPRISED AT THESE SCRIPTS.

-HMM! LOOK ALI EFFENDI! I CANT DECIPHER THIS. IF YOU WANT, TAKE IT TO THE BRITISH GENTLEMAN WORKING ON THE RAILROAD. MAYBE HE CAN READ IT.

ALI EFFENDI WENT DIRECTLY TO AYDIN AND TOOK THE SCROLL TO THE BRITISH.

-OH MY GOD! THIS IS A VERY OLD AND FANTASTIC DOCUMENT! IT IS WRITTEN IN AN ALPHABET CALLED LATIN. SIT DOWN AND I WILL DECIPHER IT FOR YOU...

THE BRITISH GENTLEMAN IMMEDIATELY STARTED TO READ AND TRANSLATE IT TO TURKISH. HE WAS GETTING MORE CURIOUS AND SERIOUS AS HE READ. IT WAS A HISTORICAL STORY AND WAS TOLD BY A YOUNGSTER. NOW, LET'S READ OUR STORY, KIDS.

-THE YEAR IS 250 A.D. MY NAME IS PULA. I AM A TEENAGER LIVING IN EPHESOS. WHEN MY FATHER MENUS WAS PASSING AWAY, I PROMISED THAT I WOULD WRITE EVERYTHING I'VE HEARD FROM OUR ANCESTORS ABOUT OUR FAMILY, THE CITY, ALL THE EVENTS I PERSONALLY WITNESSED AND LIVED THROUGH. I HOPE THAT MY CHILDREN AND THEIR CHILDREN WILL CONTINUE WRITING OUR HISTORY, SO THAT NOTHING WILL BE FORGOTTEN. I WILL START FROM WHAT WE KNOW FROM MY GREAT GRANDFATHER, THE HISTORIAN AND GEOGRAPHER **STRABON**. ONCE UPON A TIME, THERE WAS A BEAUTIFUL VILLAGE ON THE EASTERN COAST OF THE AEGEAN SEA, ON THE SKIRTS OF A MOUNTAIN. IT WAS A VERY FERTILE LAND IRRIGATED BY THE **KAISTROS** RIVER THAT FLOWED GENTLY NEARBY.

THE INHABITANTS OF THIS VILLAGE WERE THE **LELEGES**. THEY WORKED AS FARMERS, FISHERMAN, POTTERS AND WEAVERS. THEY LIVED IN PEACE FOR HUNDREDS OF YEARS BUT THEY HAD A BIG PROBLEM. THE RIVER WAS CONSTANTLY SILTING UP THE SEA AND BECAUSE OF THE MARSHES, MOSQUITOES BROUGHT DISEASES.

ONE DAY A GROUP OF WOMEN WARRIORS CALLED **AMAZONS** ARRIVED HERE ON BIG HORSES. THEY HAD BIG BOWS AND ARROWS. THEY CHOSE THIS PLACE AND THEY FOUNDED A NEW VILLAGE A LITTLE FURTHER AWAY FROM THE MARSHES BUT AGAIN ON THE SEASIDE. THEY ALSO MOVED THE INHABITANTS OF THE OLD VILLAGE HERE. THE VILLAGE WAS CALLED **EPHESOS**, AFTER THE AMAZON QUEEN.

BUT MY GRANDFATHER TOLD ME ANOTHER STORY ABOUT OUR CITY THAT HE HEARD FROM AN OLD PRIEST. THERE WAS A TRIBE CALLED **IONIANS** WHO LIVED IN THE WEST OF THE AEGEAN SEA. ONE DAY, WHEN PRINCE ANDROKLOS, THE IONIAN, WAS SAILING AND HUNTING, HE REACHED HERE WITH HIS FRIENDS.

THEY LIKED THE PLACE SO MUCH THAT THEY DECIDED TO SETTLE HERE. BUT WHERE EXACTLY? SO, ANDROKLOS SENT ONE OF HIS FRIENDS TO THE **ORACLE PRIESTESS**, WHO KNEW EVERYTHING. THE OLD WOMAN SAID:

-LISTEN MY BOY!
A FISH WILL INDICATE
THE PLACE WHERE YOU SHOULD SETTLE,
AND A WILD BOAR WILL GUIDE YOU.

ONE DAY ANDROKLOS AND HIS FRIENDS WENT HUNTING.

IN THE EVENING, WHILE THEY WERE ROASTING FISH, ONE OF THEM SKIPPED AWAY. A BOAR FRIGHTENED BY THE FISH...

...STARTED TO RUN AWAY. GRABBING HIS BOW AND ARROW, ANDROKLOS FOLLOWED THE BOAR. HE KILLED IT AT THE SKIRTS OF MT. PION NEAR THE OLD VILLAGE. HE FOUNDED THE NEW VILLAGE EXACTLY WHERE THE BOAR WAS. HE BROUGHT THE INHABITANTS OF THE OLD VILLAGE HERE.

THE NEW VILLAGE OF EPHESOS WAS SO RICH AND BEAUTIFUL THAT THE INHABITANTS LIVED THERE HAPPILY AND PEACEFULLY FOR 400 YEARS. THE VILLAGE BECAME A TOWN. IN CASE OF DANGER, THEY USED TO BAR THE HARBOR WITH A CHAIN. AS TIME PASSED BY, THE OLD GODDESS **KYBELE** BECAME **ARTEMIS** OF THE EPHESIANS. THEY BUILT A **TEMPLE** FOR HER. THAT MEANS, WE HAVE TWO STORIES TELLING US ABOUT OUR ANCESTORS.

IN THE 6. CENTURY B.C, IN PLACE OF THE SMALL TEMPLE OF ARTEMIS, THEY BUILT A HUGE AND WONDERFUL ONE ON THE COAST. THERE WAS A BIG STATUE OF ARTEMIS INSIDE. THE GREAT PHILOSOPHER **HERAKLEITOS**, WHO IS ONE OF OUR ANCESTORS, USED TO LIVE NEAR THIS TEMPLE.

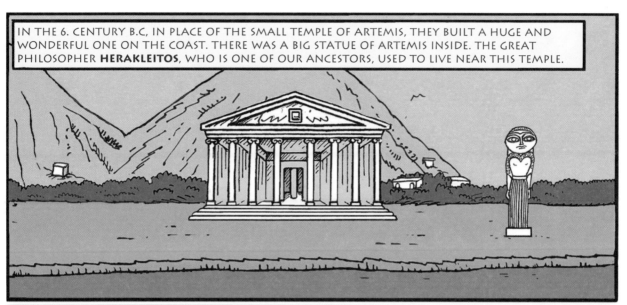

AFTER LIVING IN PEACE FOR 400 YEARS, EPHESOS WAS ATTACKED BY MANY TRIBES AND NATIONS. YET THEY STILL SURVIVED.

BUT, WHEN THE **PERSIANS** CONQUERED THE CITY, THEY STAYED HERE FOR 200 YEARS.

THE MACEDONIAN KING, ALEXANDER THE GREAT CAME TO EPHESOS IN 334 B.C. AND LIBERATED THE CITY FROM THE PERSIANS. MEANWHILE, THE HARBOR WAS FILLED WITH THE SILT CARRIED BY THE RIVER AND HAD TURNED INTO A MARSH. SO, PEOPLE WERE AGAIN VERY UNHAPPY BECAUSE OF DISEASES SPREAD BY MOSQUITOES.

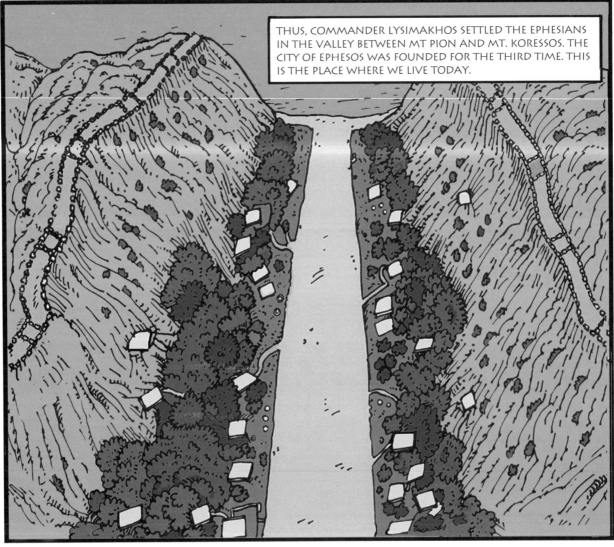

ONE DAY, A GREAT ROMAN ARMY INVADED EPHESOS AND THE ROMANS SETTLED HERE. THE CITY GREW RAPIDLY AND BECAME VERY RICH. BY THE 2. CENTURY A.D. THE POPULATION WAS ALREADY 200 THOUSAND.

EPHESOS BECAME THE MOST IMPORTANT HARBOR OF THE AEGEAN SEA. GREAT SCIENTISTS, ORATORS, ACTORS, PHILOSOPHERS POURED INTO THE CITY. EVERYDAY, DOZENS OF VESSELS DOCKED IN THE TWO HARBORS OF THE CITY DISCHARGING THEIR GOODS.

AND YOU WOULD NEVER BELIEVE HOW MANY EVENTS TOOK PLACE IN OUR TOWN. SOME OF THEM ARE VERY IMPORTANT. ABOUT 200 YEARS AGO, **ST. JOHN** BROUGHT **ST. MARY**, THE MOTHER OF JESUS, FROM JERUSALEM. SHE LIVED ON MT. PION.

ST. JOHN ALSO LIVED IN EPHESOS BUT WAS EXPELLED AND HE WENT TO THE ISLAND OF PATMOS. A FEW YEARS LATER, HIS SHIP SANK WHILE HE WAS RETURNING TO EPHESOS. HE SAILED ACROSS ON A BIG CORK. DO YOU REMEMBER THE HILL OF OUR FIRST CITY? THAT'S WHERE HE WAS BURIED WHEN HE DIED.

ST. PAUL ALSO CAME HERE. BUT, HE WAS PERSECUTED BY THE EPHESIANS. THEY DID NOT WANT HIM TO TALK ABOUT JESUS. SO, THEY IMPRISONED HIM IN A TOWER ON THE CITY WALLS. HE ESCAPED FROM THERE AFTER A WEEK.

PEOPLE WHO BELIEVE IN JESUS ARE CALLED CHRISTIANS. YOU KNOW THAT WE DON'T HAVE ONLY ONE GOD. THERE ARE TENS OF GODS AND GODDESSES: **ARTEMIS, ZEUS, ATHENA, DEMETER, NIKE, APOLLO, EROS,** AND MANY OTHERS. WE BUILD TEMPLES FOR THEM AND FOR OUR EMPERORS.

THERE ARE OTHER RELIGIONS, TOO: THE **JEWISH** RELIGION; **MITHRAISM**; **ZOROASTRIANISM** AND NOW **CHRISTIANITY**.

THIS IS ALL I KNOW ABOUT THE HISTORY OF MY TOWN. NOW I I WANT TO TELL YOU A STORY. MY OWN EXCITING ADVENTURE. IT HAPPENED IN OUR FAMILY A FEW YEARS AGO.

MY MOTHER, FATHER, AND MY BROTHER MARCUS AND I, PULA, LIVE IN THE TERRACE HOUSES ON THE CURETES STREET. THERE ARE TWO TO FIVE STORIED BUILDINGS WHERE THE RICH AND IMPORTANT PEOPLE OF THE CITY LIVE. OH, I WISH YOU COULD SEE WHAT A BEAUTIFUL CITY EPHESOS IS. THE COVERED SIDEWALKS SHINE WITH COLORFUL MOSAICS IN BEAUTIFUL DESIGNS. THE SHOPS ON THE GROUND FLOORS ARE THE FANCIEST OF THE CITY. THE MARBLE STREETS ARE ILLUMINATED WITH TORCHES AND DECORATED WITH TEMPLES AND STATUES. BUSY PEOPLE, CARTS, AND ANIMALS MOVE UP AND DOWN ALL DAY LONG. THERE ARE ALL KINDS OF ENTERTAINMENT EVERY DAY; CIRCUSES, ACROBATS, MUSICIANS, THEATERS, AND MUCH MORE. SO, THIS IS THE PLACE WHERE EVERYTHING STARTED!

THE BIG TWO-STORIED HOUSE WHERE WE LIVE, HAS A POOL IN THE ATRIUM, **FRESCOS** ON THE WALLS AND **MOSAICS** ON THE FLOORS AND SOME OF THE CEILINGS. MARCUS AND I ENJOYED PLAYING GAMES AND SOLVING RIDDLES. THE TWO SLAVES WORKING IN OUR HOUSE WERE ALSO OUR TEACHERS.

MY FATHER WAS A GREAT INVENTOR AND NEVER LEFT HIS ROOM. MY BROTHER AND I ALWAYS VISITED HIM, FOLLOWED HIS STUDIES AND CHATTED WITH HIM. HIS EYES GLOWED BRILLIANTLY AND HE RESEMBLED A GOD WITH HIS SNOW-WHITE HAIR AND BEARD.

MANY PEOPLE VISITED US EVERYDAY. MY MOTHER DIDN'T LIKE SOME OF THEM AT ALL. SOMETIMES SHE EVEN DIDN'T LET THEM IN.

THESE LAST MONTHS, MY FATHER WAS VERY EXCITED. IT WAS AS IF HE WAS KEEPING AN IMPORTANT SECRET FROM US. WE WERE VERY CURIOUS ABOUT IT. ONE DAY...

-BOYS, I AM PREPARING A SURPRISE FOR YOU. YOU HAVE TO WAIT AND BE PATIENT. I AM SURE YOU WILL ENJOY IT VERY MUCH!

MY FATHER WAS STANDING AT THE DOOR SMILING AS WE LEFT. HOW COULD WE GUESS THAT THIS WOULD BE OUR LAST CHAT WITH HIM.

-GO NOW AND ENJOY YOURSELVES, BOYS. I WILL CALL YOU WHEN I AM READY.

-UGH! I WISH HE GAVE US HIS SECRET I JUST CAN'T WAIT ANYMORE!

THE NEXT DAY OUR MOTHER CALLED US IN A HURRY. SHE WAS VERY WORRIED.

-BOYS! YOUR DAD WENT OUT LAST NIGHT AND CAME BACK VERY LATE. DID ANYONE SEE HIM THIS MORNING?

- BUT DAD NEVER GOES OUT AT NIGHT. LET'S GO AND SEE.

WE WENT TO MY FATHER'S ROOM. MY FATHER WAS LYING ON THE FLOOR.

-GOD! FOR THE LOVE OF ARTEMIS!

-DAD! DAD! WHAT HAPPENED TO YOU?

HE WAS STILL BREATHING AND MURMURING SOMETHING. A SPARK OF HOPE APPEARED IN HIS EYES WHEN HE SAW US. I PUT MY EAR ON HIS MOUTH.

-BOYS! PLAN... HIDDEN... PICTURE... BIKLET... BEE... SWARTHY!... BOX!... LIBRARY!... TALL!... MAN!... SEAL!... HERAK!... HERAK!... TRAITOR!... BEARD!

MY FATHER HAD LOST HIS CONSCIOUSNESS. HIS WORDS EXCITED US A LOT. WHAT WAS THE BIG SECRET? WHAT WAS MY FATHER'S NEW INVENTION? WHERE WAS IT? WHO WAS THE MAN? WHAT WAS BIKLET...? WE SEARCHED HIS ROOM THOROUGHLY. THERE WAS NOTHING AROUND BUT MY DAD HAD SAID, "PICTURE..."! I COULDN'T UNDERSTAND WHAT BIKLET... WAS. MAYBE THE NAME OF HIS NEW INVENTION... HE HAD PUT IT IN A CHEST AND...

-THERE IS NOTHING HERE.

-SO? BOX! LIBR...? LIBR... MUST BE THE LIBRARY. COME MARCUS! LET'S GO TO THE LIBRARY.

WE RUSHED INSIDE. SEVERAL PEOPLE SITTING AROUND THE WOODEN TABLES HAD OPENED THE PARCHMENT SCROLLS AND WERE READING SILENTLY. THERE WAS NOT A SOUND. AN OLD LIBRARIAN STANDING ON THE LADDER WAS ORGANIZING THE SCROLLS OF PARCHMENT IN THE **NICHES.**

WE PATIENTLY WAITED FOR HIM TO COME DOWN. THEN, HE CAME AND ASKED US WHAT WE WANTED. WE DIDN'T KNOW WHAT TO SAY AND WERE FRIGHTENED.

-DEAR MASTER! OUR FATHER TOLD US SOMETHING LIKE HERAK... WHAT DO YOU THINK IT IS?

-IT MUST BE HERAKLEITOS DEAR CHILDREN. THE GREAT PHILOSOPHER AND SCIENTIST. IF YOU WANT MORE INFORMATION ABOUT HIM, YOU WILL FIND IT ON THE FLOOR ABOVE.

WE WENT UPSTAIRS WITH HIM. THE NICHES WERE COMPLETELY FULL.

TAKE THIS SCROLL AND READ IT. BUT BE CAREFUL NOT TO TEAR IT.

AFTER GIVING US THE SCROLL, HE LEFT THE ROOM. WE WERE ALONE NOW. I TOLD MARCUS TO WATCH THE DOOR AND CLIMBED THE LADDER IN A RUSH. I REACHED THE NICHE WHERE THE LIBRARIAN TOOK THE SCROLL FROM.

IT WAS DARK INSIDE. I STRETCHED MY ARM LOOKING FOR SOMETHING, ANYTHING ...BUT THERE WAS NOTHING I COULD FEEL. THEN, SUDDENLY I TOUCHED SOMETHING HARD. WAS IT A BOX? PROBABLY THE BOX THAT MY FATHER HAD MENTIONED.

WE IMMEDIATELY OPENED THE BOX. THERE WAS A PIECE OF PARCHMENT IN IT.

-OH! THIS IS A SCROLL. TAKE IT AND LET'S READ IT.

WE STARTED READING IN GREAT EXCITEMENT. WE GOT GOOSE BUMPS. WE WERE PETRIFIED IN ASTONISHMENT.

Do not struggle in vain boys! It is already too late. The biklet... is mine. Do not ever follow me. I would destroy you.

SO WE WERE BEING FOLLOWED.

WE PUT THE BOX IN ITS PLACE AND WENT HOME. WE DECIDED NOT TO MENTION ANYTHING TO MOM. WE COULDN'T SLEEP ALL NIGHT.

-WHAT CAN WE DO WITH A PIECE OF PAPER IN OUR HANDS? WHO ON EARTH LEFT THE NOTE? COULD IT BE THE TALL BIG MAN WITH AN EVIL GLANCE MY FATHER MENTIONED?

WE SHOULD SOLVE THIS MYSTERY BY ALL MEANS.

I WENT TO MY DAD'S ROOM AGAIN.

-FOR THE LOVE OF ALL GODS! A CLUE! PLEASE! A CLUE!

IT WAS AS IF MY BRAIN WAS DRAINED. I LIED ON MY BED EXHAUSTED AND WENT INTO A DEEP SLEEP.

18

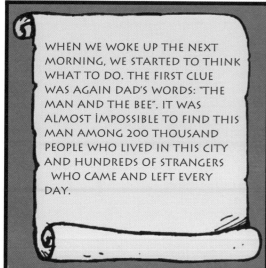

WHEN WE WOKE UP THE NEXT MORNING, WE STARTED TO THINK WHAT TO DO. THE FIRST CLUE WAS AGAIN DAD'S WORDS: "THE MAN AND THE BEE". IT WAS ALMOST IMPOSSIBLE TO FIND THIS MAN AMONG 200 THOUSAND PEOPLE WHO LIVED IN THIS CITY AND HUNDREDS OF STRANGERS WHO CAME AND LEFT EVERY DAY.

-MARCUS, WHAT DOES THE WORD BEE REMIND YOU OF?

- YOU SAY BEE? BEE! IT REMINDS ME OF HONEY AND STINGING. WHAT ELSE CAN IT BE?

SUDDENLY I HAD AN INSPIRATION! I FOUND IT.

-ISN'T THE BEE THE SYMBOL OF OUR GREAT MOTHER, THE GODDESS ARTEMIS.

WE HUGGED EACH OTHER WITH JOY!

- OFCOURSE! HURRAH, WE FOUND IT!

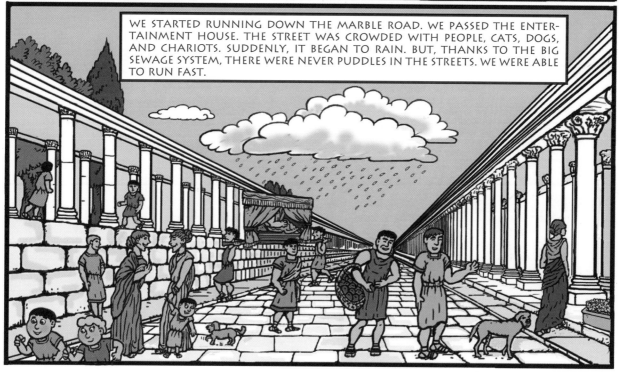

WE STARTED RUNNING DOWN THE MARBLE ROAD. WE PASSED THE ENTERTAINMENT HOUSE. THE STREET WAS CROWDED WITH PEOPLE, CATS, DOGS, AND CHARIOTS. SUDDENLY, IT BEGAN TO RAIN. BUT, THANKS TO THE BIG SEWAGE SYSTEM, THERE WERE NEVER PUDDLES IN THE STREETS. WE WERE ABLE TO RUN FAST.

WE PASSED THE AMPHITHEATER. THE MARBLE ROAD EXTENDS TO THE TEMPLE OF ARTEMIS ON THE SEASHORE. IN TWENTY MINUTES WE REACHED THE WIDE TEMPLE AREA, WHICH WAS VERY CROWDED. WE HAD BEEN THERE TWICE BEFORE. WHAT A GRAND BUILDING! MY DAD ONCE TOLD US THAT THERE ARE 127 COLUMNS INSIDE THE TEMPLE. THE PRIESTS WERE SACRIFICING ANIMALS ON THE ALTAR.

WHAT SHOULD WE DO?

IT IS FORBIDDEN TO ENTER THE TEMPLE BUT WE SLIPPED UNSEEN. ALL OF A SUDDEN, THE MAGNIFICENT STATUE OF THE GODDESS ARTEMIS APPEARED IN FRONT OF US.

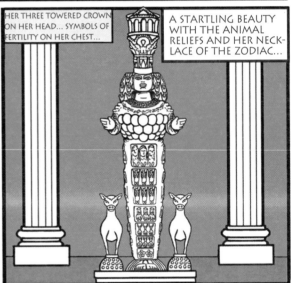

HER THREE TOWERED CROWN ON HER HEAD... SYMBOLS OF FERTILITY ON HER CHEST...

A STARTLING BEAUTY WITH THE ANIMAL RELIEFS AND HER NECKLACE OF THE ZODIAC...

THIS WAS THE MOST SACRED SPOT IN EPHESOS. WE WERE VERY EXCITED. JUST THEN...

-MARCUS! LOOK! LOOK AT THE SKIRT OF OUR GODDESS! DO YOU SEE THE BEE? THIS IS A MIRACLE!

WHEN WE SHIFTED OUR GAZES AT HER FACE...

-SHE SEEMS TO BE POINTING TOWARDS SOMETHING.

20

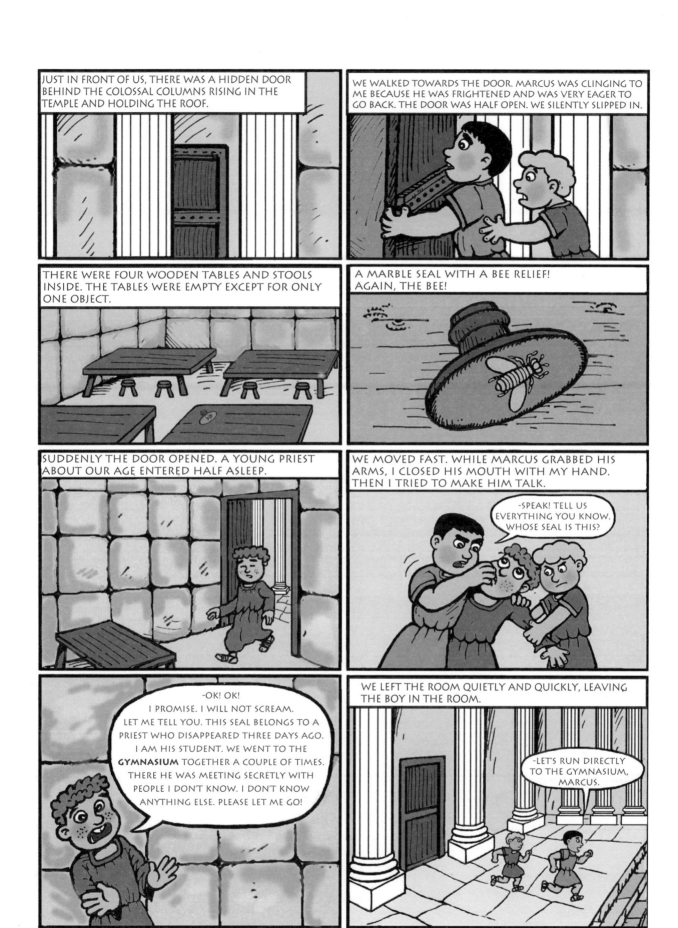

JUST IN FRONT OF US, THERE WAS A HIDDEN DOOR BEHIND THE COLOSSAL COLUMNS RISING IN THE TEMPLE AND HOLDING THE ROOF.

WE WALKED TOWARDS THE DOOR. MARCUS WAS CLINGING TO ME BECAUSE HE WAS FRIGHTENED AND WAS VERY EAGER TO GO BACK. THE DOOR WAS HALF OPEN. WE SILENTLY SLIPPED IN.

THERE WERE FOUR WOODEN TABLES AND STOOLS INSIDE. THE TABLES WERE EMPTY EXCEPT FOR ONLY ONE OBJECT.

A MARBLE SEAL WITH A BEE RELIEF! AGAIN, THE BEE!

SUDDENLY THE DOOR OPENED. A YOUNG PRIEST ABOUT OUR AGE ENTERED HALF ASLEEP.

WE MOVED FAST. WHILE MARCUS GRABBED HIS ARMS, I CLOSED HIS MOUTH WITH MY HAND. THEN I TRIED TO MAKE HIM TALK.

-SPEAK! TELL US EVERYTHING YOU KNOW. WHOSE SEAL IS THIS?

-OK! OK!
I PROMISE. I WILL NOT SCREAM.
LET ME TELL YOU. THIS SEAL BELONGS TO A PRIEST WHO DISAPPEARED THREE DAYS AGO. I AM HIS STUDENT. WE WENT TO THE **GYMNASIUM** TOGETHER A COUPLE OF TIMES. THERE HE WAS MEETING SECRETLY WITH PEOPLE I DON'T KNOW. I DON'T KNOW ANYTHING ELSE. PLEASE LET ME GO!

WE LEFT THE ROOM QUIETLY AND QUICKLY, LEAVING THE BOY IN THE ROOM.

-LET'S RUN DIRECTLY TO THE GYMNASIUM, MARCUS.

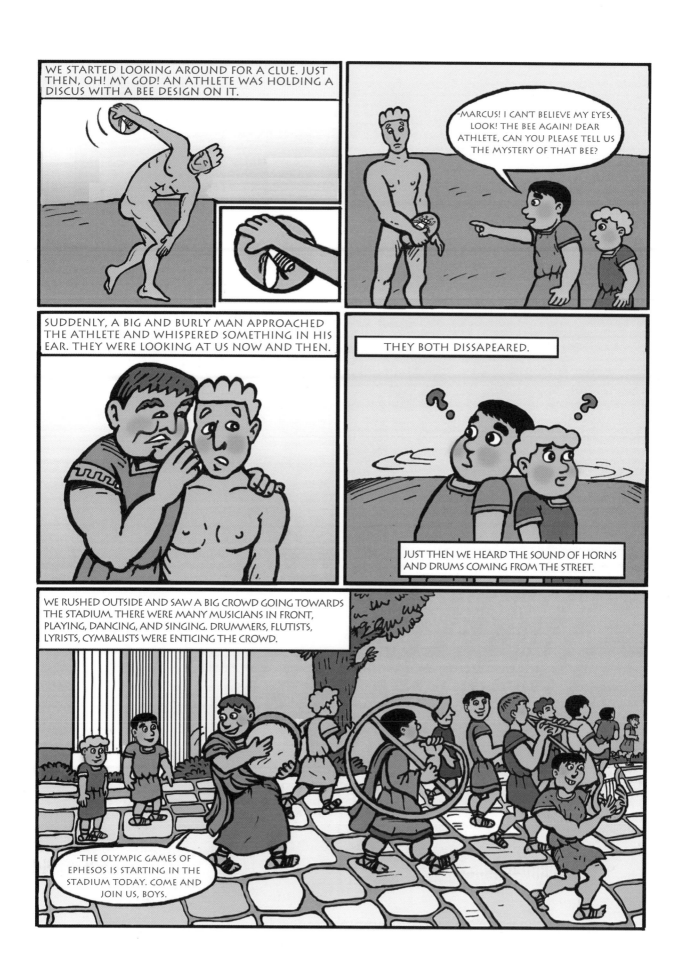

WE WENT TO THE STADIUM IN THE HOPE OF FINDING THE DISCUS THROWER. WHAT A CROWD! MAYBE THERE WERE 30 THOUSAND PEOPLE WATCHING THE GAMES. WHILE SOME ATHLETES WERE WAITING THEIR TURNS, SOME WERE RUNNING. FORGETTING OUR TROUBLES, WE STARTED WATCHING, TOO.

HOURS PASSED AND IT WAS ALREADY AFTERNOON. THE CHARIOT RACES HAD STARTED. WE WERE HAVING GREAT FUN AND WE DIDN'T EVEN LOOK AROUND.

ALL OF A SUDDEN, I FELT A PUNGENT SMELL. I REMEMBER NOTHING ELSE.

WHEN I WOKE UP, MARCUS WAS LOOKING AT ME WITH EYES SWOLLEN FROM CRYING.

-WHAT HAPPENED TO US MARCUS? WHERE ARE WE?

-IT IS VERY DARK HERE. BUT, LOOK, THERE IS A DOOR BEHIND YOU. LOOK, LIGHT IS COMING THROUGH!

-PULA, LISTEN! DO YOU HEAR FOOTSTEPS APPROACHING?

RAP! RAP! RAP!

A PEEPHOLE OPENED AND A PAIR OF BLUE EYES AND A PUFFY NOSE WAS LOOKING AT US IN ASTONISHMENT.

-FOR THE LOVE OF ZEUS, WHO IS THIS MAN?

24

THE MAN WAS TRYING TO TELL US SOMETHING WITH GESTURES. HE WAS PROBABLY DEAF AND MUTE. HE HAD A BIG KEY IN HIS HAND AND WAS POINTING TO IT.

HE GESTURED US TO FOLLOW HIM.

WE STARTED TO WALK THROUGH THE DARK LABYRINTHS.THERE WERE TUNNELS, GATES, AND COLOSSAL COLUMNS EVERYWHERE. THERE WAS NO ONE ELSE AROUND.

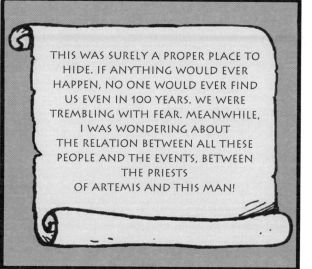

THIS WAS SURELY A PROPER PLACE TO HIDE. IF ANYTHING WOULD EVER HAPPEN, NO ONE WOULD EVER FIND US EVEN IN 100 YEARS. WE WERE TREMBLING WITH FEAR. MEANWHILE, I WAS WONDERING ABOUT THE RELATION BETWEEN ALL THESE PEOPLE AND THE EVENTS, BETWEEN THE PRIESTS OF ARTEMIS AND THIS MAN!

WE ALL STARTED CLIMBING THE NARROW AND SPIRAL STAIRS. JUST AS WE ARRIVED NEARLY TO THE TOP, THE MAN LOST HIS BALANCE AND FELL DOWN FROM THE STAIRS.

MEANWHILE, THE POOR MAN WAS LYING ON THE GROUND IN AGONY, HE OPENED HIS PALM. THERE WAS THE NUMBER SEVEN INSCRIBED ON IT.

WE DIDN'T KNOW WHAT TO DO. WE LEFT THE MAN THERE AND CLIMBED UP QUICKLY. WE WERE NOW ON THE TERRACE OF THE TEMPLE OF DOMITIANUS.

-LOOK MARCUS! LOOK AT THE BEAUTIFUL VIEW! THE DOMITIANUS SQUARE; THE POLIO FOUNTAIN AND ALL EPHESOS.

WE WENT DOWN AND REACHED THE DOMITIANUS SQUARE. WE STARTED WALKING BUT WE WERE VERY EXHAUSTED.

-I DON'T HAVE ANY ENERGY LEFT PULA. LET'S GO HOME PLEASE. MOM MUST BE WORRIED BY NOW.

-YOU ARE RIGHT MARCUS BUT WHAT IF THEY ARE FOLLOWING US. IT IS BETTER THAT WE FIND A PLACE TO SPEND THE NIGHT.

WE WALKED TO THE CAVES BEHIND MT. PION. MEANWHILE WE WERE THINKING ABOUT THE MYSTERY OF NUMBER 7. WE ARRIVED IN A CAVE. THERE WAS A ROCK AT THE ENTRANCE. WE FOUND A NARROW GATEWAY BEHIND IT.

-COME, MARCUS! THIS LOOKS LIKE A SAFE PLACE.

-IT IS SO COLD AND DARK IN HERE.

- MARCUS, WHAT CAN THAT NUMBER 7 BE?

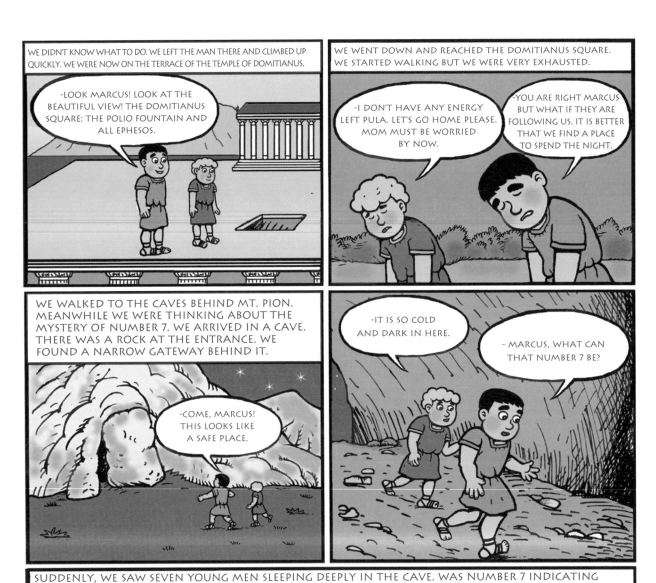

SUDDENLY, WE SAW SEVEN YOUNG MEN SLEEPING DEEPLY IN THE CAVE. WAS NUMBER 7 INDICATING THEM? THE CASE BECAME MORE COMPLICATED. IT WAS NOT CLEAR WHERE IT WAS LEADING TO. WE COULD NOT RESIST ANYTHING ANYMORE.

-HEY! GUYS! WHY ARE YOU SLEEPING HERE?

-THEY HAVE A PIECE OF IRON HANGING FROM THEIR NECKS.

THEY WERE NOT HEARING US.

WE SLIPPED THROUGH THE WALLS AND FOUND OURSELVES IN A CHAMBER WITH PAINTINGS ALL OVER THE WALLS. THERE WAS A TABLE IN THE MIDDLE AND IT WAS A MESS WITH PAINT POTS ON IT. MASKS, ACTORS AND SCENES FROM PLAYS WERE PAINTED EVERYWHERE.

WHAT COULD THE RELATION BETWEEN OUR THIEF AND THE PAINTER BE? WERE WE SET UP?

SUDDENLY, I SCREAMED WHILE EXAMINING THE PAINTING. WHAT WAS THAT? I FELT AS IF THE MAN MY FATHER DESCRIBED WAS IN FRONT OF ME.

AAAAA !

EVERYTHING STARTED TO CLEAR UP. I GUESS THE MAN WE WERE LOOKING FOR WAS AN ACTOR WHO COULD CHANGE HIS APPEARANCE ANYTIME. OF COURSE THIS FEATURE OF HIS WAS GOING TO MAKE OUR JOB DIFFICULT BUT WE HAD FOUND AN IMPORTANT CLUE.

WE RUSHED OUT FROM THE ROOM, PLACED THE ROCK IN ITS PLACE AND BEGAN TO RUN FAST.

-WE SHOULD GO OUT OF HERE QUICKLY. OTHERWISE SOMETHING WILL HAPPEN TO US.

-WHO ARE THESE MEN? LOOK, THEY ARE STILL SLEEPING.

I MADE OUR PLAN. WE WOULD GO TO THE THEATRE. IF WE HAD SOME LUCK, WE WOULD FIND OUR ACTOR THERE. BUT, WE WERE SO HUNGRY THAT WE HAD TO FIND SOME FOOD FIRST. THE MARKET AGORA WAS ON OUR WAY. SHIPS IN THE HARBOR WERE DISCHARGING THEIR LOADS, WHILE PORTERS AND DONKEYS WERE CARRYING THE GOODS TO THE AGORA. WE ENTERED THE AGORA WHERE THERE WAS A BIG CROWD. WE DID NOT WANT TO BE SEEN, SO WE HID BEHIND TWO BIG WHEAT FILLED AMPHORAE. WE WERE LOOKING AROUND TO FIND A CLUE. IT WAS TRADING TIME. AT THE CENTER OF THE AGORA, THERE STOOD A HIGH PLATFORM WITH A FEW SLAVES STANDING ON IT. THEY WERE BROUGHT BY THE SHIPS TO BE SOLD TO RICH PEOPLE. HOW BEAUTIFUL THE TEMPLE OF SERAPIS LOOKED FROM OUR CORNER! BEHIND IT, THERE WAS THE 12 KM LONG CITY WALLS WITH TOWERS AT INTERVALS. THE LAST BIG ONE WAS CALLED "THE PRISON OF ST PAUL!" WHAT A MAJESTIC VIEW!

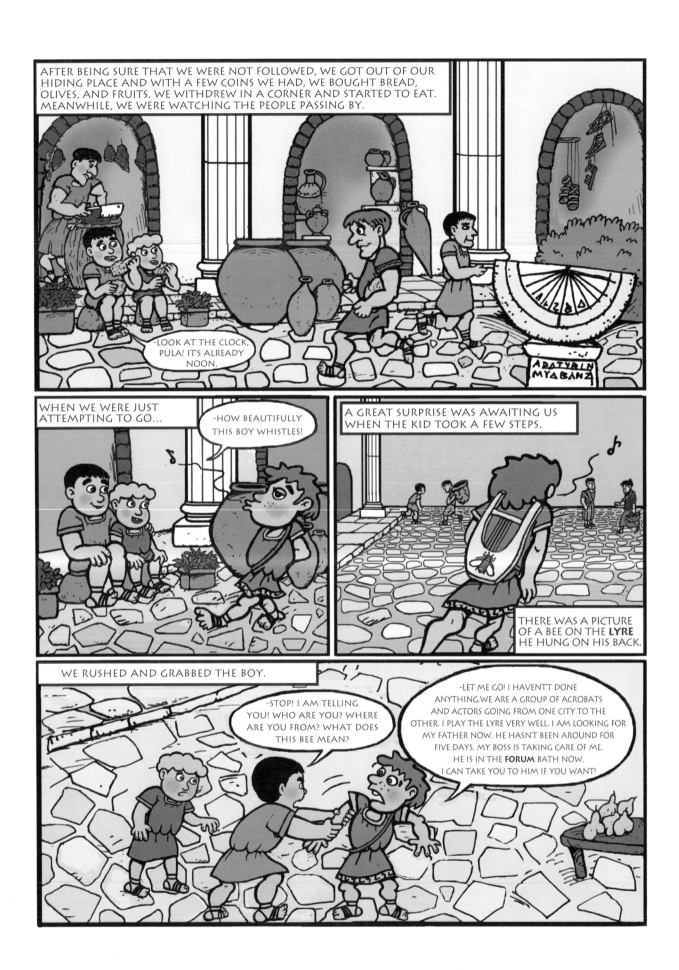

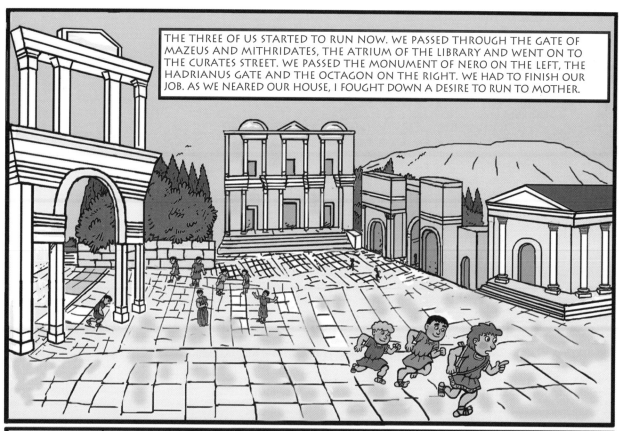

THE THREE OF US STARTED TO RUN NOW. WE PASSED THROUGH THE GATE OF MAZEUS AND MITHRIDATES, THE ATRIUM OF THE LIBRARY AND WENT ON TO THE CURATES STREET. WE PASSED THE MONUMENT OF NERO ON THE LEFT, THE HADRIANUS GATE AND THE OCTAGON ON THE RIGHT. WE HAD TO FINISH OUR JOB. AS WE NEARED OUR HOUSE, I FOUGHT DOWN A DESIRE TO RUN TO MOTHER.

WE WERE VERY TIRED AND NEEDED TO GO TO THE LATRINES. I PULLED THE BOYS' ARMS AND WE WENT INTO THE LATRINES. SEVERAL MEN WERE SITTING AND CHATTING WHILE THEY WERE DEFECATING. WE DID THE SAME AND LEFT IN A HURRY.

ONCE AGAIN WE STARTED RUNNING UP THE CURATES STREET. WE PASSED THE HADRIANUS TEMPLE. IT WAS AS IF THE BRONZE STATUES OF THE EMPERORS WERE SALUTING US.

WHEN WE REACHED THE BIG FOUNTAIN OF TRAIANUS, WOMEN WERE FILLING THEIR JUGS WITH WATER. WE REALIZED HOW THIRSTY WE WERE. WE DRANK WATER AND WASHED OUR SWEATY FACES USING THE CHANNEL IN FRONT. WE THEN CONTINUED ON OUR WAY UP.

WE CAME TO THE **HERACLES** GATE WHICH IS ONE OF THE MOST BEAUTIFUL IN THE CITY. I LOVE THESE RELIEFS. I TOUCHED HERACLES WRAPPED IN A LION SKIN. I SHOULD BECOME AS STRONG AS HIM. **NIKE**, THE GODDESS OF VICTORY IN THE MIDDLE OF THE ARCH WILL SURELY MAKE US VICTORIOUS. PASSING THROUGH THE GATE, THE MEMNIUS MONUMENT AND THE FOUNTAIN, WE REACHED THE DOMITIANUS SQUARE. THE STREETS WERE VERY CROWDED, AND IT WAS GETTING LATE. NOW WE REACHED THE SACRED FIRE OF **VESTA** BURNING IN THE STREET WITH THE **PRYTANEUM** ON OUR LEFT AND THE FORUM ON OUR RIGHT. THIS IS THE MOST IMPORTANT AREA OF EPHESOS.

WE THEN ENTERED THE BOULETARION THROUGH A BIG GATE, MEETING NO ONE. THIS IS A SMALL AUDITORIUM WHICH CAN HOLD 1400 PEOPLE. IT IS USED FOR AFTERNOON CONCERTS AND IS COVERED WITH A ROOF TO PROTECT IT FROM RAIN.

WALKING OUT, WE REACHED THE ROAD LEADING TO THE **BASILICA**.

OUR PATIENCE WAS RUNNING OUT. THE BOY LED US INTO A BIG BATH. HE WAS LOOKING FOR HIS BOSS. THE MAN WAS NOT IN THE **CALDARIUM**, NOR IN THE **TEPIDARIUM**. AT LAST WE ENTERED THE **FRIGIDARIUM**. THE BOY LOOKED AROUND AND SAW HIS BOSS IN THE POOL.

WHAT SHOULD WE DO NOW? I HAD TO THINK HARD. SHOULD THE MAN SEE US, IT WOULD BE OUR END. I PULLED THE BOY'S ARM AND WE SLIPPED OUT. IT WAS DANGEROUS TO STAY HERE NOW. MOREOVER, IT WAS ALREADY DARK OUTSIDE. WE CONVINCED THE BOY TO KEEP QUIET AND TOLD HIM IT WAS ALL A GAME. HE KEPT SILENT IN DESPERATION. WE STARTED FOR THE FORUM AND DECIDED TO SPEND THE NIGHT IN THE TEMPLE OF **ISIS**.

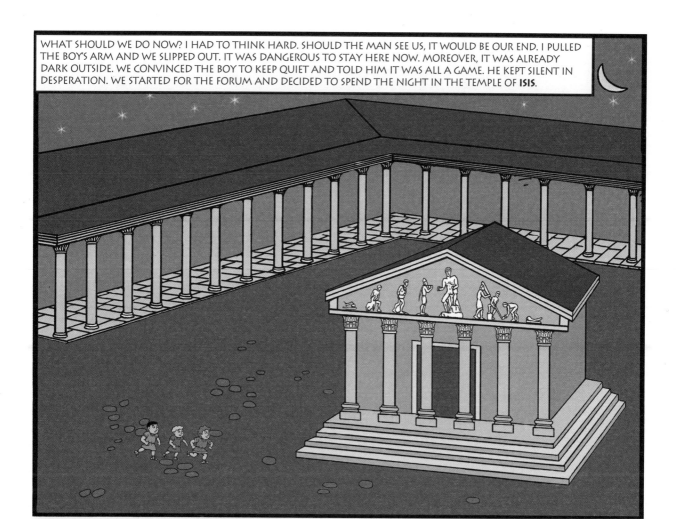

THERE WAS NO ONE AROUND. THE ISIS TEMPLE WAS IN FRONT OF US WITH ALL ITS MAGNIFICENCE IN THE MIDDLE OF A WIDE AREA. WE WERE TRYING NOT TO LOOK AT ITS PEDIMENT BECAUSE THE TERRIFYING RELIEFS OF POLYPHEMOS ALWAYS SCARED US.

THE BOY WITH US ASKED ME WHAT IT WAS. I BEGAN TO TELL TO DISTRACT HIM. 'THE KYKLOPS POLYPHEMOS, SON OF THE SEA GOD **POSEIDON**, WAS LIVING IN A CAVE ON AN ISLAND WITH HIS STOCK. THE VESSEL OF THE GREAT WARRIOR ODYSSEUS, ARRIVED IN THIS ISLAND. POLYPHEMOS IMPRISONED HIM AND ALL HIS SAILORS IN HIS CAVE. THEN HE STARTED TO EAT THEM ONE BY ONE. ODYSSEUS, OFFERED THE GIANT THE WINE HE BROUGHT FROM THE SHIP. AS THE GIANT GOT DRUNK, ODYSSEUS BLINDED HIS ONLY EYE WITH A LONG POINTED STAKE. THE SAILORS ESCAPED FROM THE CAVE BY HIDING UNDER THE SHEEP. THE STORY IS AN EXCITING ONE BUT IT FRIGHTENED US. THE BOY TOO, WAS STUNNED WITH FEAR.

WE THEN SLIPPED IN THE TEMPLE OF ISIS AND CRAWLING IN A CORNER, FELL ASLEEP.

WHEN WE WOKE UP, IT WAS DAWN. THE BOY HAD ESCAPED. OUR LIVES WERE IN DANGER NOW. THEY COULD CATCH US ANY MOMENT. EVERYTHING WAS SO COMPLICATED! WOULD THE RIDDLE BE SOLVED IF WE FOUND THE BOY? WE SHOULD BE VERY CAUTIOUS NOW. I LOOKED AROUND AND SAW LIGHT COMING FROM AHEAD. WHEN I WALKED THERE, I SAW TORCHES HANGING ON THE WALL. I TOOK ONE OF THEM AND STARTED EXAMINING THE PLACE.

I STOPPED IN FRONT OF THE SHELVES WHERE SMALL FIGURINES WERE. IT WAS AS IF SOMETHING WAS GOING WRONG.

WHILE I WAS LOOKING AT THE SHELVES, I REALIZED THAT THERE WAS SOMETHING BEHIND THEM. I REMOVED THE BOTTOM SHELF. IT WAS AS IF A STONE WAS HIDING A SECRET GATEWAY.

WHEN WE MOVED THE STONE, IT OPENED LIKE A DOOR AND WHEN WE HELD THE TORCH INSIDE, WE COULDNT BELIEVE WHAT WE SAW. IT WAS AN ARCHIVE CHAMBER!

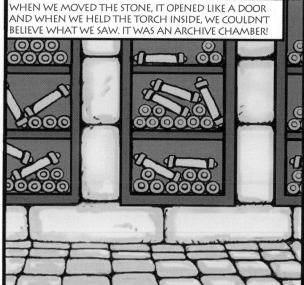

WE ENTERED WITH CAUTION. BUT NOW OUR CURIOUSITY AND EXCITEMENT TOOK THE PLACE OF FEAR. SUDDENLY WE JUMPED WITH A SOUND.

IT WAS COMING FROM BEHIND THE WALL.

I TRIED TO OPEN A HOLE ON THE WALL WITH THE BROKEN LEG OF A TABLE. AFTER LONG EFFORTS...

...A PAIR OF PLEADING BLUE EYES, LOOKING AT US. WHO WAS THIS MAN?

WE STARTED TO CRY WITH JOY AND TOLD HIM THAT WE WERE THE SONS OF THIS INVENTOR AND THAT OUR FATHER WAS SICK. LEAVING THE MAN THERE AND GOING BACK THE SAME WAY, WE USED THE SHORT CUT TO THE THEATER. RIGHT ACROSS OUR HOUSE, THERE IS A BIG STAIRWAY BY THE BATHS OF SKOLASTIKA. WE CLIMBED THE STEPS QUICKLY. REACHING THE TOP, WE SLIPPED INSIDE THE THEATER THROUGH THE **VOMITORIUM**. THERE WAS A BIG CROWD WAITING FOR THE PERFORMANCE TO START. ABOUT 24 THOUSAND PEOPLE! TODAY THERE WAS NO MUSICIANS, NO ACTORS WITH MASKS, AND NO GLADIATORS. WHAT WAS NEW TODAY?

UNFORTUNATELY, IT WAS IMPOSSIBLE FOR US TO CATCH HIM. WHEN AT LAST WE HAD REACHED THE SHORE, THE MAN WAS ALREADY SAILING ON A BOAT WITH THE BIKLETTA. THE MAN FOLLOWING US HAD DISSAPEARED ALSO. WE COLLAPSED ON THE SHORE AND BEGAN TO CRY. THERE WAS NOTHING WE COULD EVER DO ANYMORE. IT WAS GETTING DARK AND THE CLOUDS IN THE SKY WERE INCREASING.

ALL AT ONCE, A STORM BROKE AND THE LIGHTENINGS WERE FRIGHTENING. DESPERATELY, WE TOOK REFUGE BEHIND THE ROCKS NEARBY AND FELL ASLEEP.

WHEN IT WAS DAWN. THE RAIN HAD STOPPED AND THE SKY WAS CLEAR. WE RAN TO THE SHORE. ALAS! WHAT DO YOU THINK WE SAW? BROKEN PIECES OF WOOD; A SEAL WITH A BEE RELIEF; AND A PIECE OF PARCHMENT WITH FADED SCRIPTS AND DESIGNS... BIKLETTA'S PLANS. THE BIKLETTA ITSELF WAS BROKEN TO PIECES. THE THIEF WAS PROBABLY DROWNED. WHAT A PITY! WHAT A LOSS! MY FATHER'S INVENTION, HIS GIFT TO HUMANITY, WAS GONE FOREVER. BUT, MAYBE TOMORROW, OR HUNDREDS OF YEARS LATER, ANOTHER INVENTOR WILL REINVENT THIS MACHINE. THIS IS MY PERSONAL STORY AND ALL I HAVE TO WRITE. I HOPE, OUR CHILDREN WILL KEEP ON WRITING OUR HISTORY.

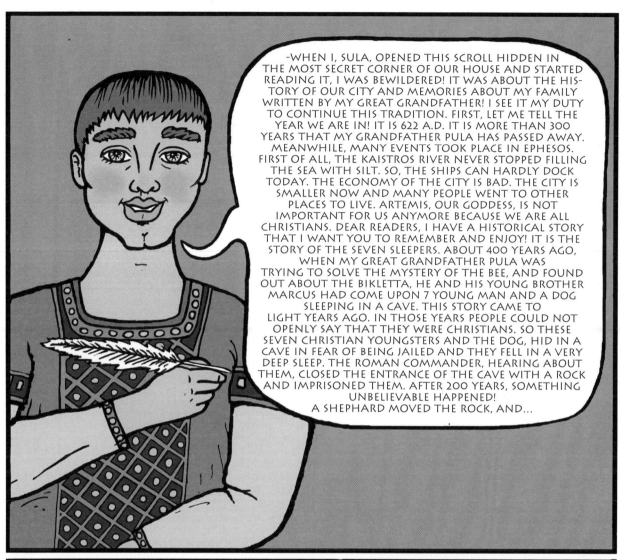

-WHEN I, SULA, OPENED THIS SCROLL HIDDEN IN THE MOST SECRET CORNER OF OUR HOUSE AND STARTED READING IT, I WAS BEWILDERED! IT WAS ABOUT THE HISTORY OF OUR CITY AND MEMORIES ABOUT MY FAMILY WRITTEN BY MY GREAT GRANDFATHER! I SEE IT MY DUTY TO CONTINUE THIS TRADITION. FIRST, LET ME TELL THE YEAR WE ARE IN! IT IS 622 A.D. IT IS MORE THAN 300 YEARS THAT MY GRANDFATHER PULA HAS PASSED AWAY. MEANWHILE, MANY EVENTS TOOK PLACE IN EPHESOS. FIRST OF ALL, THE KAISTROS RIVER NEVER STOPPED FILLING THE SEA WITH SILT. SO, THE SHIPS CAN HARDLY DOCK TODAY. THE ECONOMY OF THE CITY IS BAD. THE CITY IS SMALLER NOW AND MANY PEOPLE WENT TO OTHER PLACES TO LIVE. ARTEMIS, OUR GODDESS, IS NOT IMPORTANT FOR US ANYMORE BECAUSE WE ARE ALL CHRISTIANS. DEAR READERS, I HAVE A HISTORICAL STORY THAT I WANT YOU TO REMEMBER AND ENJOY! IT IS THE STORY OF THE SEVEN SLEEPERS. ABOUT 400 YEARS AGO, WHEN MY GREAT GRANDFATHER PULA WAS TRYING TO SOLVE THE MYSTERY OF THE BEE, AND FOUND OUT ABOUT THE BIKLETTA, HE AND HIS YOUNG BROTHER MARCUS HAD COME UPON 7 YOUNG MAN AND A DOG SLEEPING IN A CAVE. THIS STORY CAME TO LIGHT YEARS AGO. IN THOSE YEARS PEOPLE COULD NOT OPENLY SAY THAT THEY WERE CHRISTIANS. SO THESE SEVEN CHRISTIAN YOUNGSTERS AND THE DOG, HID IN A CAVE IN FEAR OF BEING JAILED AND THEY FELL IN A VERY DEEP SLEEP. THE ROMAN COMMANDER, HEARING ABOUT THEM, CLOSED THE ENTRANCE OF THE CAVE WITH A ROCK AND IMPRISONED THEM. AFTER 200 YEARS, SOMETHING UNBELIEVABLE HAPPENED! A SHEPHARD MOVED THE ROCK, AND...

THESE YOUNG MEN WHO FELL ASLEEP IN 250 A.D....

...WOKE UP IN 448 A.D. THEY WERE NOT AWARE THAT THEY SLEPT FOR 200 YEARS.

THEY WERE VERY HUNGRY. SO, ONE OF THEM WENT TO THE AGORA TO BUY FOOD.

-A LOAF OF BREAD PLEASE!

-WHAT'S THAT? WHAT KIND OF MONEY IS THAT? YOU KNAVE!

UPON COMPLAINTS, THE SOLDIERS CAUGHT THE YOUNG MEN AND BROUGHT HIM BEFORE THE GOVERNOR.

-HMM! I DIDN'T UNDERSTAND ANYTHING. LET'S GO AND LOOK IN THE CAVE.

THE GOVERNOR CAME INTO THE CAVE WITH THE YOUNG MEN.

WHEN THEY ENTERED THE CAVE, THEY FOUND A SCROLL IN A SEALED CHEST, TELLING HOW THE YOUNG MEN HAD DIED. UPON THIS, A CHRISTIAN PRIEST BLESSED THEM.

THE NEXT DAY, THE SEVEN YOUNG MEN WENT BACK TO SLEEP IN THE CAVE FOREVER. THIS CAVE IS A HOLY PLACE FOR US AND MANY CHRISTIANS ARE BURIED HERE.

I HAVE ANOTHER IMPORTANT STORY FOR YOU. REMEMBER THE TOMB OF ST. JOHN. YEARS AFTER HE DIED, THE EPHESIANS BUILT A CHURCH AROUND HIS TOMB. AND A FEW YEARS AGO, THE GREAT EMPEROR JUSTINIANUS AND HIS WIFE THEODORA BUILT A HUGE BASILICA IN THE SHAPE OF A CROSS AROUND THE CHURCH. MANY FAMILIES IN EPHESOS MOVED HERE. THERE ARE GREAT WALLS AROUND THE BASILICA.

THE TOWN AROUND THE BASILICA OF ST. JOHN IS GROWING DAY BY DAY. A CASTLE WAS BUILT ON THE HILL AND AQUEDUCTS WERE ERECTED TO CARRY WATER TO THE TOWN IN THE 5. CENTURY.

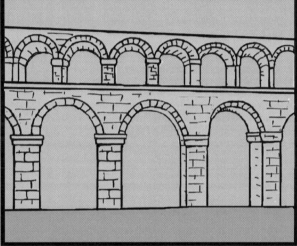

A CHURCH WAS BUILT ON MT. PION WHERE ST. MARY, THE MOTHER OF CHRIST LIVED. ALL THE CHRISTIANS GO THERE OFTEN FOR PILGRIMAGE. THIS IS GOING TO BE MY LAST STORY. THERE IS NO MORE PLACE LEFT ON THIS PARCHEMENT. MAYBE ONE DAY MY CHILDREN WILL CONTINUE WRITING OUR HISTORY SOMEHOW.

THE BRITISH GENTLEMAN FINISHED READING THE SCROLL.

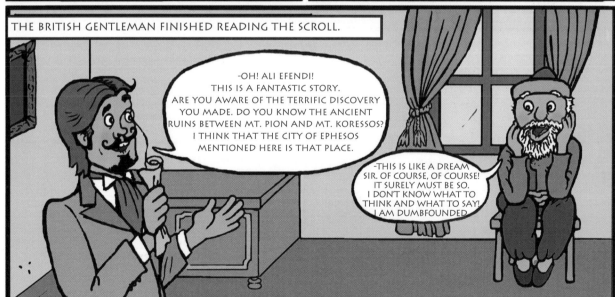

-OH! ALI EFENDI! THIS IS A FANTASTIC STORY. ARE YOU AWARE OF THE TERRIFIC DISCOVERY YOU MADE. DO YOU KNOW THE ANCIENT RUINS BETWEEN MT. PION AND MT. KORESSOS? I THINK THAT THE CITY OF EPHESOS MENTIONED HERE IS THAT PLACE.

-THIS IS LIKE A DREAM SIR. OF COURSE, OF COURSE! IT SURELY MUST BE SO. I DON'T KNOW WHAT TO THINK AND WHAT TO SAY! I AM DUMBFOUNDED.

FIN

What is Mythology?

People of ancient civilizations, believed in many gods and goddesses. Mythology is the legends heard, told or written about gods, semi-gods and heroes. They are tales, epics, stories, and myths. Every nation on earth has it's own myths and epics. Two greatest epic writers of the West are **Homeros** from İzmir (ancient Smyrna) and **Hesiodos** from Kyme (Aliağa). Homeros, who wrote the first mythological stories in history, is the writer of two great works: The *Iliad* and the *Odysseus*, written around the 8. century B.C. They are about the Trojan wars (**the Trojan Horse**) and their sequences that took place in the 12. century B.C.

Cevat Şakir Kabaağaçlı known as the **Fisherman of Halicarnassos** (Bodrum), is a famous Turkish story and fiction writer. He is a real Turkish academician who collected and interpreted all the mythological information and wrote books about them. **Azra Erhat** is another great writer who followed the footsteps of his masters, the Fisherman and Sabahattin Eyüboğlu. She wrote books about the history and archaeology of Turkey with the purpose of introducing the treasures of the country. His "**Glossary of Mythology**" is his masterpiece.

GLOSSARY OF MYTHOLOGY

Amazon: women warriors; fight on horses; use bows, arrows and the symmetrical double headed ax called the labrys.

Aphrodite (Venus): the goddess of love and beauty.

Apollo (Apollo): the god of light and reason; also represents youthful manly beauty and associa-ted with music, archery, and medicine who also sees the future.

Artemis (Diana): Apollo's twin sister, virgin hunteress.

Artemis of Ephesos (Diana): goddess of fertility, moon, universe, and animals. She is one of the mother goddesses.

Asklepios: god of health; considered as the father of all doctors.

Athena (Minerva): goddess of war and patron of arts and crafts; represents intelligence, wisdom, and power of thought.

Demeter (Ceres): goddess of fertility; of wheat and corn.

Dionysos (Bacchus): god of agriculture and wine; ancestor of all performance arts.

Eros (Cupid): god of love; depicted as a little boy with wings, and an arrow with a bow in his hands.

Hades (Pluto): the god of the underground.

Heracles (Hercules): most popular of Greek heroes representing strength; always trying to do good deeds and depicted as clad in lion skin.

Hermes (Mercury): the messenger god with a broad brimmed hat and winged sandals and a magical wand to show the way to travellers and traders; he invented the lyre with 7 strings.

Hestia (Vesta): the hearth goddess protecting homes and families, and the state with an eternal burning fire.

Isis: mother goddess of old Egypt.

Kybele: the mother goddess of Anatolia.

Medusa: one of the three fairy sisters with braided hair of snakes who keeps the evil eye away.

Nike (Victoria): the goddess of victory with wings.

Oracle woman (Sybil): a woman who can see the future and can tell the fortune of a person in the temples of Apollo.

Poseidon (Neptune): god of the seas who makes the waves with his triton.

Serapis: god of the dead in old Egypt.

Tykhe (Fortuna): goddess of luck, fortune.

Zeus (Jupiter): god of the sky and father of all gods.

GLOSSARY OF ARCHAEOLOGY AND BASIC INFORMATION

A.D. (Anno Domini): after the brith of christ; the year of his brith is the first year.

Acropolis: highest peak of ancient cities; sometimes it is a castle where important buildings and temples are located.

Agora (Forum): market place in ancient cities; open area in antique Greek cities where commercial and formal activities took place; called as forum in ancient Rome.

Amphora: large storage jars with a narrow mouth, two handles and usually a pointed base.

Anatolia: the big peninsula in Asia called Turkey.

Aqueducts: arches invented by the Romans and built to transfer water from distant sources with a channel on them where the water flowed.

Arcade (stoa): a range of arches covered on top.

Arch: a flat or curved construction on two columns.

Archaeology: a branch of science revealing and examining the historical remains from ancient ages; mostly the works are excavated from under the ground; ones working in this field are called **archaeologists**.

Archive: old documents and the places where they are kept.

Atrium: the open court of a Roman house.

Basilica: big rectangular court hall of the Romans; also the church built in the same style.

Bath: a Roman invention; has a few divisions; *frigidarium* is the cold room with a pool; *tepidarium* is the warm room; *caldarium* is the hot room; further there are other rooms such as dressing, sweating, massage, and perfume rooms.

Bouleterion: Greek and Roman senate house.

B.C.: the years before the birth of Christ.

Capital: the head or crowning member of a column. There are four styles of capitals in Ephesos: Doric, Ionic, Corinthian, and composite.

Column: an upright cylindrical or rectangular member made of wood or stone erected to hold a roof or for decorative purposes.

Consuls: the highest public officers elected every year in ancient Rome.

Cymbal: a musical instrument made of two big round metal pieces.

Fresco: painting made on wet plaster.

Gladiator: warrior athletes who fought with each other or with wild animals in amphitheatres, staduims or circuses during the Roman Period.

Gymnasium: a kind of school or academy where education was given.

Kaistros: Küçük Menderes River.

Labyrinth: endless and complex corridors.

Latin: formal language of the Roman Empire; the origin of many European languages; the alphabet we are using today is the Latin one.

Lyre: an ancient musical instrument with strings; the number of strings can be 4, 7, or 11.

Macedonia: a region in the Balkans in Europe.

Marble: a kind of stone used for building or decoration.

Megaron: an ancient building type with a rectangular plan with a hearth in the center.

Mosaic: panels on the floors or walls made of small colored stones or glass.

Narthex: a plant with a long stem used as a torch; also the main entrance of a church.

Niche: a cavity carved in the wall.

Odeon: a roofed building used for musical performances.

Orator: one who relates interesting subjects to the public with a very beautiful style of speech.

Palaestra: open training area in the gymnasiums.

Parchment (Pergamon): there was no paper in ancient days. Very thin animal skin was used for that purpose after it was specially treated.

Persians: the ancient people of Iran.

Prytaneum: meeting place of the senate committee where also ambassadors were recieved and where the sacred hearth with the eternal fire of goddess Vesta burned.

Scroll: rolled parchment or paper. There were no paged books or book-binding in old days. Documents were kept in this way.

Selçuk (Seljuk): a town of İzmir. Turks arrived here at the beginning of the 12. century. While Seljuk was first invaded by the Menteşe Principality, the Aydınoğulları Pirincipality captured it later. It was first caled Ayasuluk and was made the capital of the pirincipality by Hızır Bey; İsa Bey improved the city. The Mosque of İsa Bey built in 1375, is the largest in the pirincipalities. The ruins of Ephesos, The Temple of Artemis and the Basilica of St. John are situated here.

Site: the area where the ruins or remains of ancient cities, castles buildings can be found.

Stoa: roofed portico walled at the back with columns in front; sometimes with shops behind.

Strabon: a Roman geographer and historian who lived in the 1. century (64/63 B.C.-19 A.D.).

Temple: a big building built for a god, goddess or emperor in ancient times.

Tribe: a group of people who belong to the same lineage.

Vault: a roof or ceiling of stone or brick usually built in the shape of a half-cylinder.

Vomitorium: the vaulted passages in Roman theaters.

Glossary of Religion in Ephesos

Idol: a figure or item resembling a god that is worshipped.

Judaism: first monotheistic religion; the prophet is Moses; the place of worship is the Synagogue; the priest is a rabbi; worshippers are called Jews.

Christianity: monotheistic religion; the prophet is Jesus Christ; the place of worship is the church; the priest or pastor is in charge of the church; worshippers are called Christians.

Islam: monotheistic religion; the prophet is Mohammed; place of worship is the mosque; the priest is the imam; worshippers are called Moslems.

St. Mary (Virgin Mary): mother of Christ.

Saint John: one of the 12 apostles of Christ.

Saint Paul: the person who extensively spred the Christian religion. He was born in Tarsus-Turkey.

Mithraism: an ancient Persian religion; worshipped the gods of light, integrity and fire.

Biklet-Bikletta

The word was used instead of bicycle. The bicycle was not invented by the Romans. The story in this book is only imaginary. British Lawson invented it in 1879. In 1885 Starley designed the one we use today.

EPHESOS

N	W	V	I	R	G	I	N	M	A	R	Y	W	Z
Q	O	Y	X	R	E	Q	D	C	S	F	M	T	J
M	L	E	N	N	D	E	O	N	G	G	N	S	T
H	Z	E	D	H	P	H	W	J	W	X	M	U	J
I	S	A	M	O	S	A	I	C	I	N	J	M	R
N	K	M	M	U	E	I	U	E	T	A	R	P	Z
J	V	A	R	O	G	A	A	R	T	E	M	I	S
S	R	X	E	H	T	R	A	N	P	B	S	U	G
F	Z	M	Q	T	N	E	M	H	C	R	A	P	G
I	Z	R	H	J	O	C	S	E	R	F	C	H	B
B	H	Q	M	U	I	S	A	N	M	Y	G	V	P
Y	E	B	A	S	İ	U	R	H	I	G	O	D	O
K	C	E	M	T	F	H	E	R	A	C	L	E	S
C	E	D	V	N	M	U	L	O	C	I	C	D	D

WORD

HUNT

Can you find the words below among the letters above?

Agora	Column	Heracles
Artemis	Virgin Mary	Gymnasium
Fresco	Mosaic	Odeon
İsa Bey	Narthex	Parchment

Let's See What We Have Learned

1. Where is the site of Ephesos?
2. What are the women warriors called?
3. One of the Seven Wonders of the Ancient World is in Ephesos. What is it called?
4. Between which mountains is the site of Ephesos located?
5. What is an agora/forum?
6. How many main streets are there in Ephesos? What are their names?
7. How many people could the theatre hold?
8. What are the names of the two important buildings beside the market agora?
9. How many types of column capitals are found in Ephesos? What are they called?
10. Where can you see frescos in Ephesos?
11. Where can you see mosaics in Ephesos?
12. Tell three monuments built in the name of the Roman emperors in Ephesos.
13. Tell two names important for Christianity?
14. What is on Mt. Pion that belongs to Virgin Mary?
15. Who is the great goddess of Ephesos?
16. Who is Hestia / Vesta?
17. How many harbors are there in Ephesos?

18. What was the population of Ephesos?

19. When were the city walls of Ephesos built? Who built them and how many kilometers long were they?

20. What is the name of the god clad in lion skin?

21. Who is the goddess with snake hair?

22. Where do you find a caldarium, tepidarium, frigidarium?

23. Why was Ephesos abandoned?

24. Where is the Church of St. John?

25. What is the old name of Selçuk?

26. What is the name of the big mosque in Selçuk?

27. What is the name of the village on the mountain where some of the inhabitants of Ephesos settled after the city was abandoned?

28. What is parchment?

29. What is the title of the episode that took place in the cave behind Mt. Pion?

30. When was the bicycle invented?

Answers:

1. Selçuk, İzmir, **2.** Amazon, **3.** Artemis Temple, **4.** Mt. Pion and Mt. Koressus, **5.** market place, market area or meeting place, **6.** 3, Curates, Marble and Arkadian, **7.** 24 thousand, **8.** Celsus Library, **9.** 4 types, Doric, Ionian, Korinthean, composite, **10.** slope houses, **11.** slope houses, **12.** Hadrianus Temple, Traianus Fountain, Domitianus Temple, **13.** St. John, Christ, St. Paul, Virgin Mary, **14.** her home, **15.** Artemis - Diana, **16.** protector of the city, homes, goddess of the hearth, **17.** 2, **18.** about 200-250 thousand **19.** by Lysimakhos in 4. century B.C., **20.** Heracles, **21.** Medusa, **22.** Roman baths, **23.** Because the harbor turned into a marsh and there was malaria, **24.** in Selçuk, **25.** in Ayasuluk, **26.** İsa Bey Mosque, **27.** Şirince (Kırkınca), **28.** paper made of animal skin, **29.** 7 sleepers, **30.** 1789.

Notes

Erdemgil S., *Yamaç Evler*, p.1 Atalar Matbaacılık, İstanbul.

Özeren, Ö., *Ephesus*, Keskin Color Kartpostalcılık, İstanbul 1991.

Selected Bibliograpy

Agizza, R., *Antik Yunan'da Mitoloji*, (trans. Z. İlkgelen) Arkeoloji ve Sanat Yayınları, İstanbul 2006.

Akurgal E., *Anadolu Uygarlıkları*, İstanbul 1995.

Başgelen, N., *Güneşin Bahçesi Anadolu*, Arkeoloji ve Sanat Yayınları, İstanbul 1996.

Cimok, F., *Biblical Anatolia*, A Turizm Yayınları, İstanbul 2000.

Erhat, A., *Mitoloji Sözlüğü*, Remzi Kitabevi, İstanbul 1989.

Erdemgil, S., *Yamaç Evler*, Atalar Matbaacılık, İstanbul.

Özeren, Ö., *Ephesus*, Keskin Color Kartpostalcılık, İstanbul 1991.

Saltuk, S., *Arkeoloji Sözlüğü*, İnkilap Kitabevi, İstanbul 1989.

Schmeider, E. E., *Ephesus and Pergamon, Past and Present*, Vision Roma.

Türkoğlu, S., *Efes'in Öyküsü*, Arkeoloji ve Sanat Yayınları, İstanbul 1999.